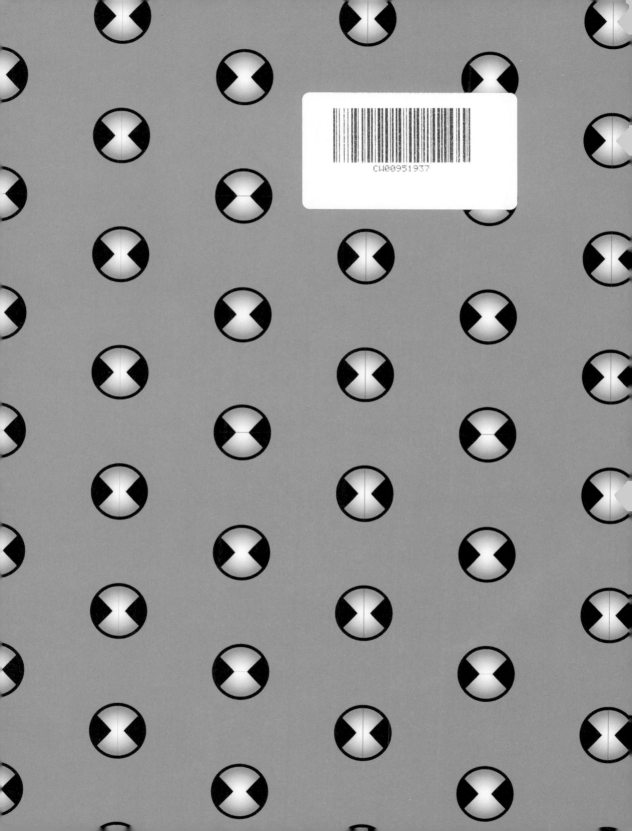

BEN 10 HANDBOOK
A CENTUM BOOK 978-1-911460-20-6
Published in Great Britain by Centum Books Ltd
This edition published in 2017.
1 3 5 7 9 10 8 6 4 2

Ben 10, CARTOON NETWORK, the logos, and all related characters
and elements are trademarks of and © Cartoon Network. (s17)

Centum Books Ltd, 20 Devon Square,
Newton Abbot, Devon, TQ12 2HR, UK
books@centumbooksltd.co.uk

CENTUM BOOKS Limited Reg. No. 07641486

A CIP record of this book is available from the British Library.

Printed in China

BEN 10

HANDBOOK

WELCOME!

THIS BOOK BELONGS TO :

ZAK

Ben 10 and his aliens are always saving
the day (normally because they've
caused the havoc themselves!).

In this book you will learn about all of the
Ben 10 characters and with your special
Ben-tastic skills complete some mysterious
puzzles and defeat some terrible villains.

It's hero time!

MEET THE FAMILY!

Grandpa Max

Ben

Ben, Gwen and Grandpa Max shoot around the country in their trusty transport the Rustbucket. They've had countless adventures on their travels and there are going to be many more if Ben has his way!

Rustbucket

Gwen

MEET THE ALIENS!

All of Ben's aliens have different amazing features but he can't always choose who he turns into!

Introducing...

Cannonbolt

Diamondhead

Four Arms

Grey Matter

Heatblast

Overflow

Stinkfly

Upgrade

Wildvine

XLR8

9

ALL ABOUT BEN 10

He's stubborn, funny, clever, quick-thinking and a little bit messy – just like your average ten-year-old!

Favourite thing to do (apart from turning into an alien superhero!): play video games

Ben Tennyson is just a normal kid... who happens to be able to turn into a superhero – ten of them!

10

OMNITRIX, ACTIVATE!

This is Ben's Omnitrix.
Each time he presses
it he turns into a
different alien.

Draw your own Omnitrix – what features does it have?

13

ALL ABOUT
Cannonbolt

Planet of origin

Arburia

Superpower

Invulnerable sphere
– he can roll himself
into a ball and cause
serious havoc.

Weakness

No trouble getting
started but sometimes
finds it hard to stop.

Cannonbolt is one powerful alien – he can run trucks off the road and knock people over.

He also has sharp claws which help with tricky foes!

That's one awesome water bomb!

Yes, everybody loves getting soaked.

Anything he can rebound from can be used by this alien. Ricocheting off surfaces gives him extra power!

ALIEN DOODLE!

If you had aliens, what would they be like?

Planet of origin
_____

Superpower
_____
_____
_____

Weakness
_____
_____
_____

Planet of origin

_____

Superpower

_____
_____
_____

Weakness

_____
_____

17

ALL ABOUT
Diamondhead

Planet of origin
Petropia

I'm solid like a rock!

Superpower
Crystal weaponry and structures.

Weakness
He can shatter and crack if enough force is applied.

Diamondhead is made from hard silicone – diamond-hard!

Makes diamond structures to stand on and conquer villains.

He shoots diamond shards from his hands.

He can reflect light and energy beams back to his foes.

CRYSTAL TOWER

His crystal structures are super fireproof.

He can enclose villains with his crystals – making a diamond-hard prison!

WHICH ALIEN ARE YOU?

Take this quiz to find out.

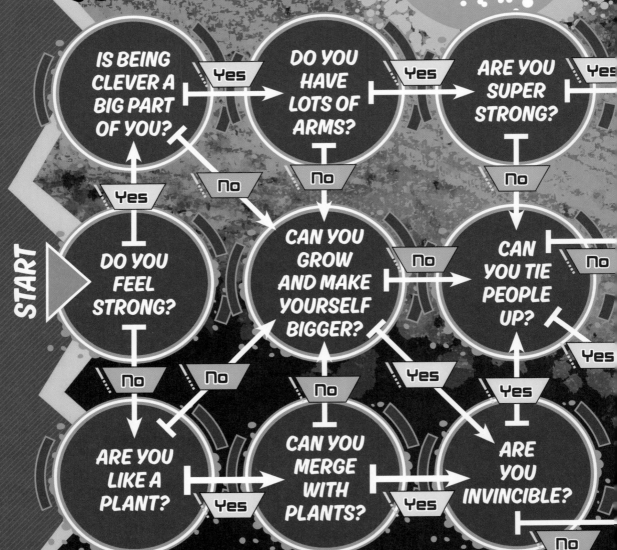

START

IS BEING CLEVER A BIG PART OF YOU?

Yes → DO YOU HAVE LOTS OF ARMS?

Yes → ARE YOU SUPER STRONG?

Yes

No (from Is being clever) → CAN YOU GROW AND MAKE YOURSELF BIGGER?

No (from Do you have lots of arms) → CAN YOU GROW AND MAKE YOURSELF BIGGER?

No (from Are you super strong) → CAN YOU TIE PEOPLE UP?

Yes (back up to Is being clever) — DO YOU FEEL STRONG?

DO YOU FEEL STRONG?

No → ARE YOU LIKE A PLANT?

No → CAN YOU GROW AND MAKE YOURSELF BIGGER?

CAN YOU GROW AND MAKE YOURSELF BIGGER?

No → CAN YOU TIE PEOPLE UP?

No (down) → CAN YOU MERGE WITH PLANTS?

Yes → ARE YOU INVINCIBLE?

CAN YOU TIE PEOPLE UP?

No

Yes → ARE YOU INVINCIBLE?

ARE YOU LIKE A PLANT?

Yes → CAN YOU MERGE WITH PLANTS?

CAN YOU MERGE WITH PLANTS?

Yes → ARE YOU INVINCIBLE?

ARE YOU INVINCIBLE?

Yes (up) → CAN YOU TIE PEOPLE UP?

No

20

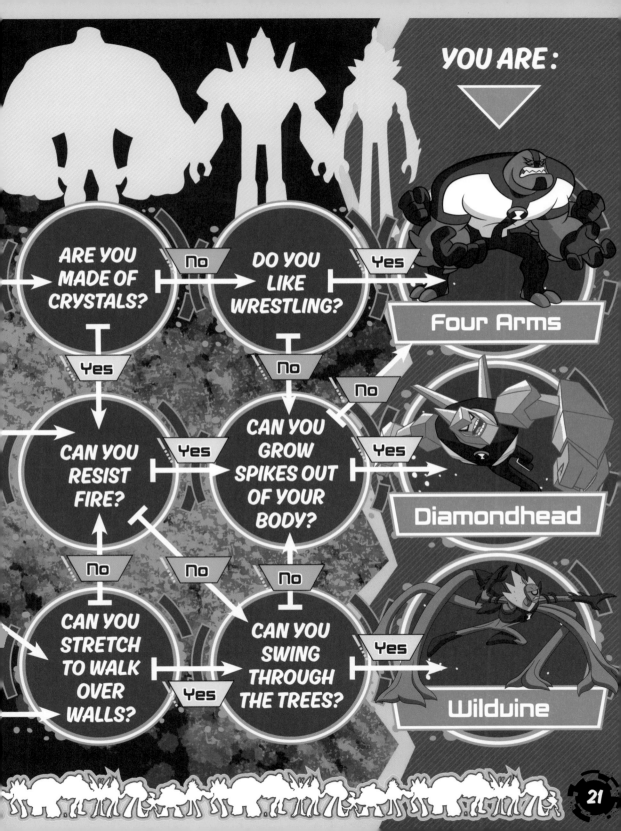

YOU ARE:

ARE YOU MADE OF CRYSTALS?

No

DO YOU LIKE WRESTLING?

Yes

Four Arms

Yes

No

No

CAN YOU RESIST FIRE?

Yes

CAN YOU GROW SPIKES OUT OF YOUR BODY?

Yes

Diamondhead

No

No

No

CAN YOU STRETCH TO WALK OVER WALLS?

CAN YOU SWING THROUGH THE TREES?

Yes

Wildvine

Yes

ALL ABOUT Four Arms

Planet of origin
Khoros

Superpower
Super strong.

Weakness
Not the fastest alien!

Hey, who are you calling slow?

Erm, no one, sir!

He's four times as strong as the most powerful alien in the galaxy.

With his four arms he packs an almighty punch, again, and again, and again and again!

He can lift the heaviest of objects.

He can deliver the most powerful of punches.

He can create shockwaves by slapping his hands together.

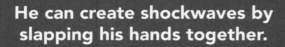

PUZZLE THIS!

Can you find the missing pieces of the puzzle to complete it? If only Grey Matter were here to help!

a.

b.

c.

d.

e.

f.

g.

h.

i.

j.

k.

l.

See answers on page 92.

25

ALL ABOUT
Grey Matter

Planet of origin
Galvan Prime

What I'm lacking in brawn I make up for in brains!

Superpower
Super smart technophile.

Weakness
Small and therefore not as strong as the other aliens.

Grey Matter is the smartest of them all! He needs to use his complex brain since he can't use brute force like the other aliens.

He's a complete technophile and able to figure out how complex machines work.

With his clever micro suction cups he's able to walk up wires.

When Grandpa Max gets eaten by a monster he's able to use his knowledge of the body to rescue him.

He looks like a grey frog but don't underestimate the little guy!

WHO'S THE HERO?

Only one of these is the real Ben 10. Can you work out which it might be?

See answers on page 92.

ALL ABOUT
Heatblast

Planet of origin

Pyros

Superpower

Ability to control fire.

Weakness

Can't shoot fireballs in water.

You forgot magnetic personality and charming good looks!

Groan!

noo

Heatblast has control over heat-based blasts and is able to throw fire from his hands.

He can make fireballs and throw them a long way!

He can jump high into the air using fire as a propeller.

He can surf and fly on fire – that's a cool way to get around!

He can absorb heat and fire into himself.

BEN'S PORTRAIT!

Draw Ben 10 from this picture grid.
Try to copy him exactly!

LET'S DO THIS!

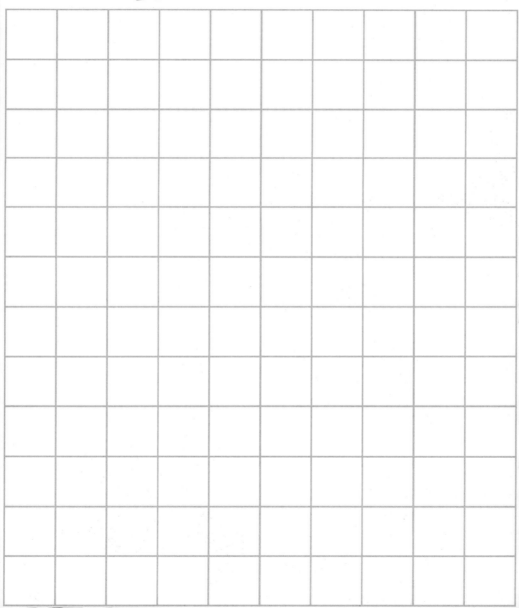

ALL ABOUT Overflow

Planet of origin
Kiusana

I also have charming green eyes and no rust!

OK, cool it!

Superpower
Ability to control water.

Weakness
Unknown.

Overflow can control most forms of moisture, which when you think the Earth is pretty much covered in water, is a lot!

He can harden water into a protective exoskeleton form.

Waterblasts propel him along and waterjets help him fly.

He shoots water from his arms.

As well as creating whirlpools he can redirect water – which can come in handy!

CODEBREAKER!

Ben is trying to work out what Gwen is saying.

???

A / P	B / Q	C / R	D / S
E / T	F / U	G / V	H / W
I / X	J / Y	K / Z	L / A
M / B	N / C	O / D	P / E
Q / F	R / G	S / H	T / I
U / J	V / K	W / L	X / M
Y / N	Z / O		

T UFDE
DLH SPI!

ANSWER:

_____

_____

CREATE YOUR OWN
SECRET MESSAGE:

_____

_____

_____

_____

_____

ALL ABOUT Stinkfly

Planet of origin
Lepidoptera

Superpower
High-speed flying.

Weakness
Not so good on the ground!

He sometimes gasses himself by mistake!

 Hey, that was only once... or twice!

This flying super alien hero can shoot gases and goos from his eyes and his mouth. They're highly flammable and unbearably stinky!

He flaps his wings to spread poisonous gases.

He can use his arms and punch bad guys if needed!

The stink he can create is so bad it can break ice and structures.

39

RUSTBUCKET

This has transported Ben, Gwen and Grandpa Max on hundreds of adventures!

Draw your own transport! Will you want to sleep and eat in it too?

ALL ABOUT
Upgrade

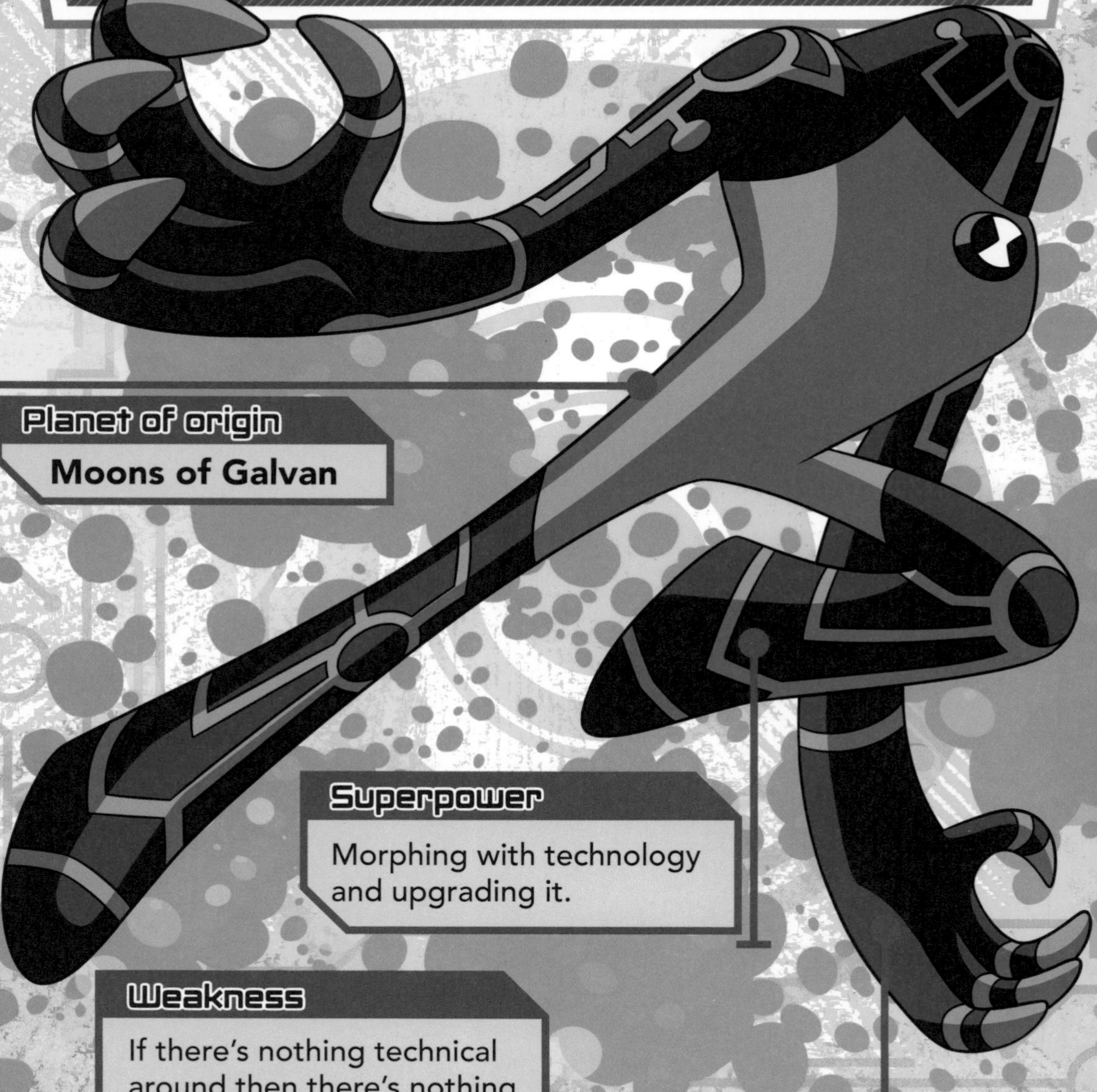

Planet of origin

Moons of Galvan

Superpower

Morphing with technology and upgrading it.

Weakness

If there's nothing technical around then there's nothing for him to do!

42

Upgrade's nanotechnology body can pour itself over any piece of technology, merge with it and upgrade it instantly.

He's quite the escapee, with a cunning trick of turning into liquid and then back again into solid form.

For the slickest, coolest machines - call Upgrade.

 And the lawnmower?

That was cool!

Reversing the power so baddies can't fire is another great party trick!

DON'T WAKE THE DRAGON!

Heatblast's decided to take a little trip underground but no one told him there is a dragon asleep down here. Help him retrace his steps before it wakes up! Too late – run!!

START ▷

44

PHEW!

FINISH

See answers on page 92.

ALL ABOUT
Wilduine

Planet of origin
Flors Verdance

Superpower
Ability to grow and retract super strong vines.

Don't get your vines in a tangle!

That hardly ever happens!

Weakness
He can get hurt.

Wildvine can merge with any plant on the planet.

He can dig through the earth and regenerate himself.

He can tie people up with his vines and swing around on them too.

He can stretch his vines to walk over walls and make plants grow super quickly.

His vines can cut metal and he can also shoot small vines at villains if needed.

HIDDEN TREASURE!

Try and help Ben and Gwen get to the cave with the treasure before all the villains do! Follow the directions – hurry!

	1	2	3	4	5	6	7
A	START ▽						
B							
C							
D							
E							
F							
G							
H							

KEY:
⬇ DOWN
⬆ UP
⬅ LEFT
➡ RIGHT

DIRECTIONS:

1 ⬇ ,4 ➡ ,6 ⬇ ,3 ⬅ ,
2 ⬆ ,2 ➡ ,5 ⬆ ,6 ➡ ,
3 ⬇ ,4 ➡ ,4 ⬇ ,2 ⬅ ,
3 ⬆ ,4 ➡ ,3 ⬆ ,2 ⬅ .

THE TREASURE IS IN SQUARE:

10	11	12	13	14	15	16

See answers on page 92.

49

ALL ABOUT
XLR8

Planet of origin
Kinet

Weakness
Not that strong!

Superpower
Super speedster.

He's not very good at running on ice!

Hey! You try it with balls on your feet.

He can go 500+ mph and is very effective at going in for the attack.

He can also affect the weather with his speed – look at him whipping up a tornado!

XLR8 can manipulate friction and travel at some crazy fast speeds!

GUESS WHO?

Write their names once you guess who each alien is from their close-up.

1

2

3

4

5

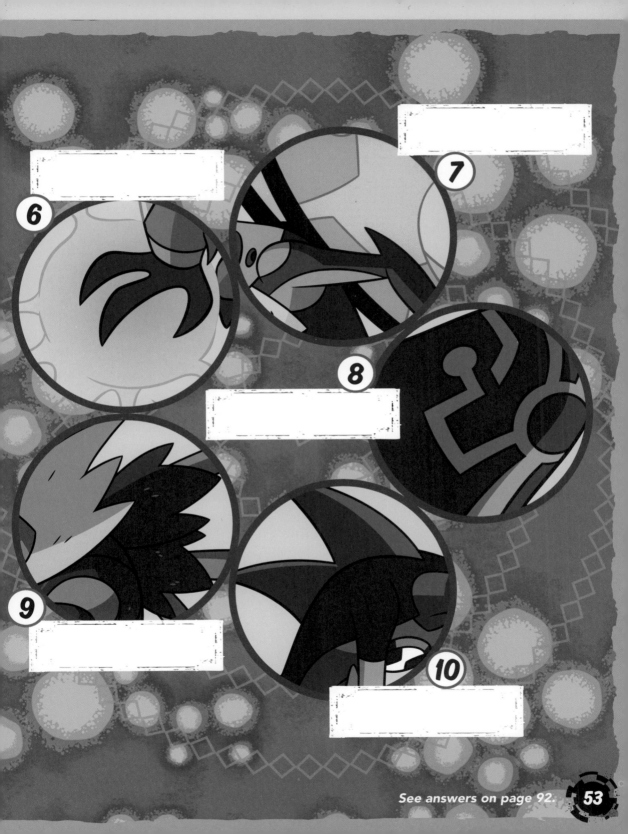

6

7

8

9

10

See answers on page 92.

ALL ABOUT GWEN

Gwen Tennyson is 10 years old, like Ben. She's Ben's closest cousin.

She's often the voice of reason for Ben, although Ben finds it hard to listen to her. Thankfully she has a good sense of humour!

When Gwen was changed into Ben, and Ben was changed into Gwen, by the evil Hex she panicked and was worried she couldn't be an alien superhero. But with a little help from Ben she did fine.

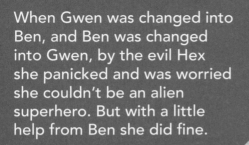

 She also has bad breath.

No, I don't.

 Your pet puppy agrees with me.

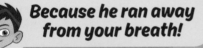 I don't have a pet puppy.

Because he ran away from your breath!

Gwen's always at Ben's side to lend a helping hand, whether it's filming an action movie for him, playing him at video games or trying to wake him up so he doesn't sleepwalk in alien form.

QUIZ TIME!

1. **What's Ben's surname?**

   _____

2. **Where do Grandpa Max, Ben and Gwen sleep?**

   _____

3. **Which alien can shoot fire?**

   _____

4. **What does Ben activate to turn into an alien?**

   _____

5. **Who can tie people up with vines?**

   _____

56

6. **The fastest alien is?**

_____

7. **The strongest alien is?**

_____

8. **The cleverest alien is?**

_____

9. **The hardest alien is?**

_____

10. **The only alien who can roll himself into a sphere is?**

_____

See answers on page 92.

ALL ABOUT GRANDPA MAX

Grandpa Max is probably the only adult who could handle the complicated duo of Ben and Gwen.

He doesn't panic and faces the endless dangerous situations they find themselves in with a calm head.

Funniest saying: "Hold on to your guacamole folks!" (As he roars the Rustbucket out of the way of the Weather Heads.)

He can't help but get super excited about old stuff from the past – cue an eye roll from Gwen and Ben! And when he tries to dance they find it super embarrassing!

Is that how they danced in the olden days?

It's the most I've ever seen Grandpa Max move!

He takes Ben and Gwen to some amazing places and they always have an extraordinary time – just not always quite what he plans!

SHADOWY ALIENS

Can you identify each alien
by their shadow? You hero!

1

2

3

4

See answers on page 93.

ODD ONE OUT

This line-up is not quite right – who shouldn't be here?

ANSWER:

See answers on page 93.

GWEN'S SUDOKU

Gwen has set Ben a sudoku puzzle! Draw the correct picture in each square. There must only be one of each picture in each row, column and square.

You're not allowed to call Grey Matter to solve it.

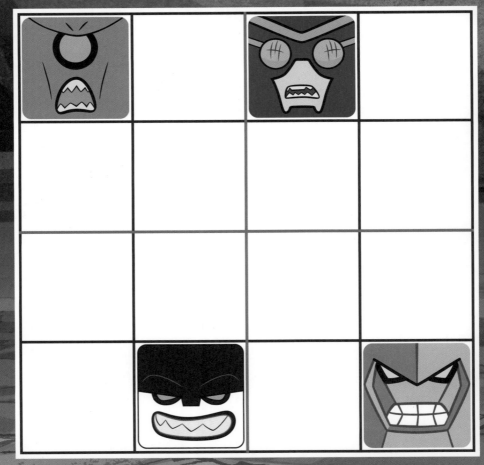

See answers on page 93.

WHAT'S THE STORY?

Write your own
Ben 10 scenes!

Boredom level

GWEN'S MESSAGE

Ben's left a message for Gwen! Follow the circle in a clockwise direction and write down every third letter in the spaces to read the secret message.

START

K O M G
I R P Q U E P
L Z K N H E H
T W N E H S
E C B T
Z T O P
A M O A
D T Q
U L T T R U
P B U
E I O M E R T

Message:

See answers on page 93.

WHIZZ AT NUMBERS!

Gwen's got to finish the sums and get to the gold before the villains do. Each answer leads to the next sum which will take you down to gold - or if you get them wrong something more yucky!

$$2 + 6 =$$

8		4

$$3 + 7 = \qquad 9 - 5 =$$

6		10		4

$$7 + 7 = \qquad 2 \times 2 = \qquad 3 - 2 =$$

14		4		1		9

$$10 - 5 = \qquad 5 \times 2 = \qquad 3 + 3 = \qquad 9 + 4 =$$

10		6		13		5

Gold

Flames

Cactus

Stinky Mess

See answers on page 93.

IT'S HERO TIME!

Play the game and try and get to the middle before the villains get you! Roll the dice and move along the board – watch out!

18 Ben is in a tricky situation with a dragon. Go back two steps.

19

20

21 Heatblas is saving the day Go forwa two space

17

32

33 Here comes Diamondhead! Go forward one space.

34

16

31

30 Ben and Gwen are swinging high! Go back four places.

29

15 Do you feel the need for speed? XLR8 will run you forward four spaces.

14

13

12 Grey Mat is a bit to small for t Go bac one spac

2

3

Here comes Cannonbolt. Go forward four spaces!

4

ART

23

24

Cannonbolt's got slightly tied up! Go back two spaces.

5

36

FINISH

25

6

Uh-oh! Stinkfly is behind bars. Go back one space.

27

Overflow has caught the bad guy! Go forward two spaces.

26

7

10

9

Four Arms has got the baddies! Move forward one space!

8

THE VILLAINS!

Name	Hex
Race	Human
Planet of Origin	Earth
Occupation	Magician
Special Powers	Magical Mayhem

Name	Zombozo
Race	Human
Planet of Origin	Earth
Occupation	Creepy Clown
Special Powers	Hypnosis

Name

Dr Animo

Race

Human

Planet of Origin

Earth

Occupation

Mad Scientist

Special Powers

Genetic Genius (can manipulate DNA)

Name

Steam Smythe

Race

Human

Planet of Origin

Earth

Occupation

Inventor

Special Powers

Chaotic Inventions

Name

La Grange

Race

Human

Planet of Origin

Earth

Occupation

Evil Racing Car Driver

Special Powers

Lightning-fast Reflexes and Mechanical Gadgetry

ALIEN PLANET

Diamondhead comes from the alien planet, Petropia. Draw what you think it looks like.

Petropia

CLONED!

Grandpa Max has been cloned b
some villains. Help Ben and Gwe
round all of his clones up! How
many Max clones are there?

THERE ARE

GRANDPA MAX CLONES.

See answers on page 93.

BUZZ OFF!

Where are the giant bugs going? Help Ben find his way to the Queen Bee.

START

FINISH

See answers on page 93.

DRAW US!

Finish off Stinkfly and Overflow.

Stinkfly

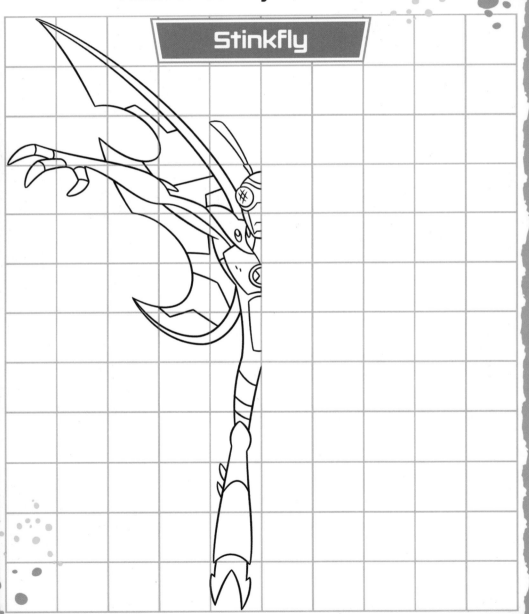

Overflow

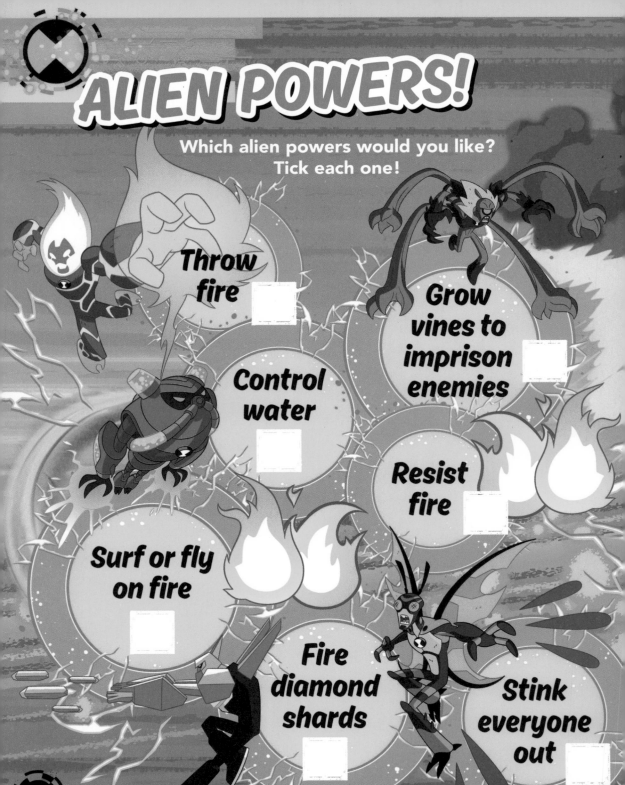

ALIEN POWERS!

Which alien powers would you like?
Tick each one!

Throw fire

Grow vines to imprison enemies

Control water

Resist fire

Surf or fly on fire

Fire diamond shards

Stink everyone out

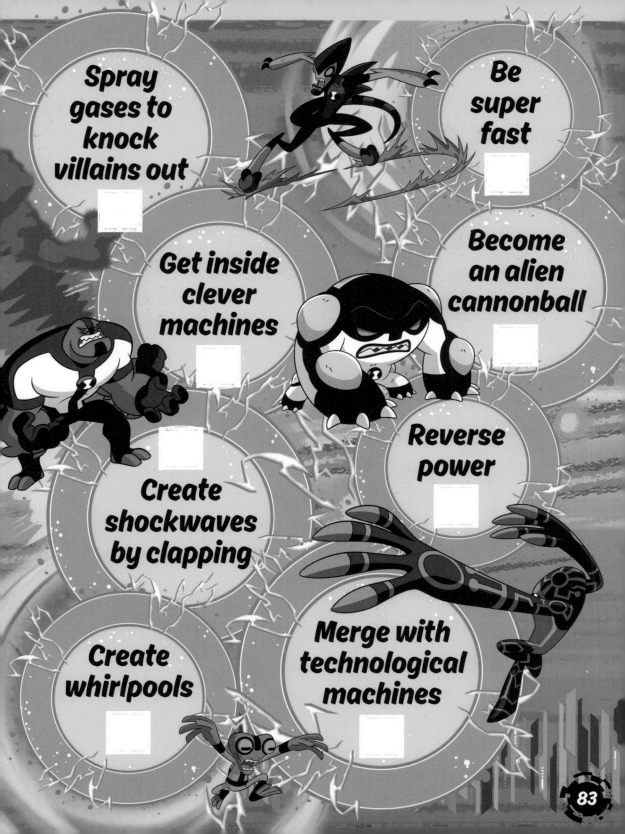

Spray gases to knock villains out

Be super fast

Get inside clever machines

Become an alien cannonball

Reverse power

Create shockwaves by clapping

Create whirlpools

Merge with technological machines

83

JOKE TIME!

I refuse to be made a fool by you insolent brats!

Ha! Ha! We don't even know what insolent means!

Four Arms is funny too, when he's in the wrestling ring with Iron Kyle.

One side tomato can!

Tomato can? Did he just canned fruit me?

ALIEN NAME GENERATOR!

Which alien name will you have?

Take the day of the month you were born.

(if it's a double digit use the last one).

0. Speed
1. Shadow
2. Lightning
3. Sonic
4. Storm

5. Orange
6. Optical
7. Green
8. Rocket
9. Strong

Take the month of your birthday.

1. Vine
2. Bottom
3. Cloud
4. Head
5. Space
6. Boom
7. Orbit
8. Moon
9. Strike
10. Frame
11. Race
12. Crystal

FIRST NAME:

SECOND NAME:

87

SPOT THE DIFFERENCE!

Can you find ten differences between these pictures? Use some alien powers and you'll be done in no time!

88

See answers on page 93.

WHICH ALIEN?

1. A villain is trying to shoot fire at you...

 **A**  **B**  **C**

2. You need to get over a wall...

 **A**  **B**  **C**

3. You need to modify a vehicle...

 **A**  **B**  **C**

4. You need to blast through something...

 **A**  **B**  **C**

5. It's the strongest villain you've ever seen...

 **A**  **B**  **C**

6. You need to get inside a machine...

 A
 B
 C

7. It's time to cause a dreadful stink...

 A
 B
 C

8. You want to create a whirlpool....

 A
 B
 C

9. You want to build something really hard...

 A
 B
 C

10. You need to get somewhere super fast...

 A
 B
 C

See answers on page 93.

ANSWERS

PAGE 24-25 - PUZZLE THIS!

1. = d.   2. = f.   3. = b.
4. = k.   5. = g.   6. = j.

PAGE 28-29 - WHO'S THE HERO?

PAGE 36-37 - CODEBREAKER!

Gwen is saying:

I JUST SAW HEX!

PAGE 44-45 - DON'T WAKE THE DRAGON!

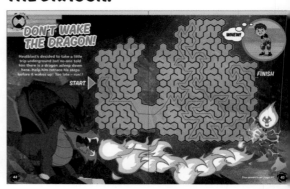

PAGE 48-49 - HIDDEN TREASURE

PAGE 52-53 - GUESS WHO?

1. Diamondhead   2. Cannonbolt
3. Grey Matter   4. Four Arms
5. Heatblast   6. Overflow
7. Stinkfly   8. Upgrade
9. Wildvine   10. XLR8

PAGE 56-57 - QUIZ TIME!

1. Tennyson   2. The Rustbucket
3. Heatblast   4. Omnitrix
5. Wildvine   6. XLR8
7. Four Arms   8. Grey Matter
9. Diamondhead   10. Cannonbolt

PAGE 60-61 - SHADOWY ALIENS

1. Grey Matter
2. Diamondhead
3. Heatblast
4. Stinkfly
5. Upgrade
6. Cannonbolt
7. Four Arms
8. Overflow
9. XLR8
10. Wildvine

PAGE 62-63 - ODD ONE OUT

Hex

PAGE 64 - GWEN'S SUDOKU

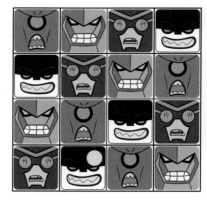

PAGE 65 - TANGLED LINES

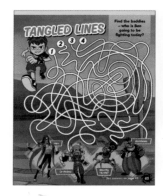

PAGE 68 - GWEN'S MESSAGE

Ben's message says 'Meet me at Rustbucket.'

PAGE 69 - WHIZZ AT NUMBERS!

PAGE 76-77 - CLONED!

There are 27 Grandpa Max clones.

PAGE 78-79 - BUZZ OFF!

PAGE 88-89 - SPOT THE DIFFERENCE!

PAGE 90-91 - WHICH ALIEN?

1. A
2. B
3. C
4. B
5. A
6. A
7. C
8. A
9. C
10. B

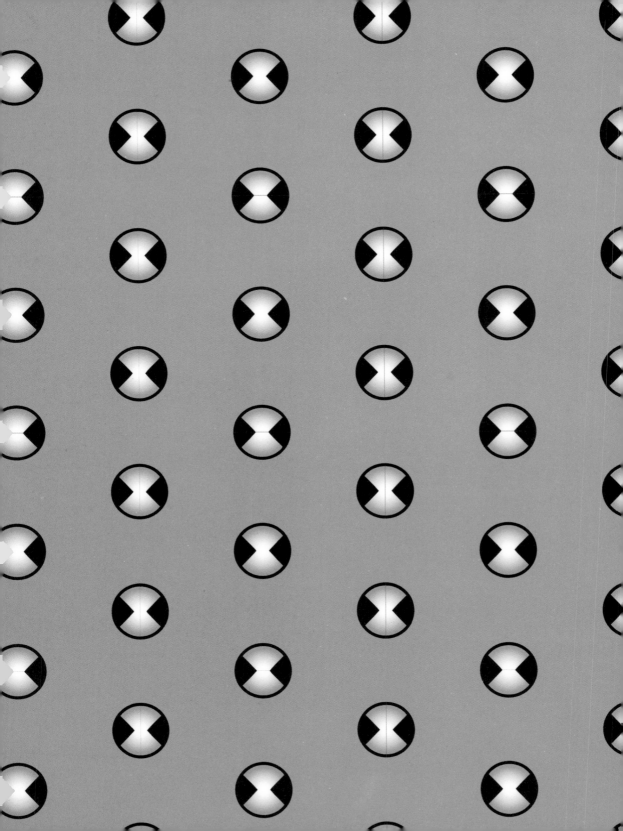